Starting Recovery with Relapse Prevention

A Workbook by Terence T. Gorski

Based on the GORSKI-CENAPS® Model

Starting Recovery with Relapse Prevention

A Workbook by Terence T. Gorski

Based on the GORSKI-CENAPS® Model

Produced by The CENAPS Corporation
6193 Deltona Blvd.
Spring Hill, FL 34606
Phone: (352) 596-8000
Fax: (352) 596-8002
E-mail: *info@cenaps.com*

Herald Publishing House/Independence Press
P.O. Box 390
Independence, MO 64051-0390
Phone: 1-800-767-8181 or (816) 521-3015
Fax: (816) 521-3066
Website: *www.relapse.org*

Training Contact
For training information contact: (352) 596-8000 or e-mail *info@cenaps.com*.

Contents

Introduction

If everything were going well in your life, you would not be reading this workbook. So, let's face the facts. You have developed problems because of your use of alcohol, prescription medication, or other drugs. Your doctor or another healthcare provider has recommended that you stop using drugs. That health professional wants you to stay abstinent during the early stages of recovery and hopefully as an ongoing lifestyle choice.

You have a hard decision to make. *Are you willing to face the truth about your alcohol or other drug use and act accordingly?* If you are willing to make a personal commitment to stop using alcohol and other drugs, this workbook will help. Please approach the information and complete the exercises with an open mind. The exercises in this workbook should be completed under the supervision of your doctor or therapist. It is not meant as a substitute for proper medical or professional treatment.

The goal of this workbook is to help you stay away from alcohol or other drugs during the early stages of recovery. First, let's review some terms used in treatment and recovery from addiction:[1]

1. **Alcohol and Other Drugs:** This term includes: (1) alcohol in all of its forms including beer, wine, hard liquor, and over-the-counter medications, such as cough and cold remedies, that contain alcohol as an ingredient; (2) potentially addicting prescribed medications, unless specifically prescribed by the doctor treating your addiction and used exactly as prescribed; (3) illicit or illegal drugs; and (4) mood-altering drugs you can buy over the counter. Ask your doctor or therapist for a specific list of medications you need to stop using.

2. **Abstinence:** Completely stopping the use of alcohol and other drugs as described in point one above.

3. **Sober (Sobriety):** To be sober (that is, to get into sobriety) means more than just being abstinent. It means learning the skills that will improve your health, solve your life problems, and allow you to find a sense of meaning and purpose in your life without the need to use alcohol or other drugs.

4. **Addiction:** The use of alcohol or other drugs that causes physical, psychological, or social problems. Addicted people find they are unable to stop using alcohol and other drugs despite the problems being caused by using alcohol and other drugs. Addiction is a catch-22 in which using alcohol and other drugs give you short-term relief from the pain and problems caused by your use of alcohol and other drugs. You are probably addicted if a doctor or therapist has ever recommended that you stop using alcohol or other drugs because it would make a physical or psychological problem worse and you did not follow the recommendation.

5. **Treatment:** Treatment consists of the specific activities recommended by and supervised by your doctor or therapist involved in the treatment of your addiction.

6. **Recovery:** What you do on your own to stay abstinent and improve the quality of your sobriety, such as going to recovery support meetings, reading recovery literature, or doing special activities like completing the exercises in the workbook.

7. **Relapse:** The process of becoming dysfunctional in recovery that is related to increased stress, craving, habitual drug-seeking behavior, and using alcohol or other drugs despite your commitment to stay abstinent.

Addiction is a complicated illness that affects you physically, psychologically, and socially. Recovery is a long-term process that proceeds in steps and stages.[2] You learn to get abstinent, manage cravings, break free from denial and addictive thinking, and improve the quality of sobriety over time.

You cannot do this process alone! You are going to need the help of your doctors; other addiction professionals including psychologists, social workers, therapists, and counselors; your family and friends; and the recovery support groups recommended by your doctor or therapist.

This is a quick guide to staying in recovery during the early stages without relapsing back to the use of alcohol or other drugs. First, look at the table of contents and page through the workbook. Then complete the exercises in the order they are presented. Discuss your progress and problems with your doctor or therapist. With proper treatment from your doctor, help from a therapist, and the exercises in this workbook, you will learn how to start feeling better and improve the quality of your life. The first step is to get a better understanding of addiction.

Exercise 1:
The Morning Plan and Evening Review

The purpose of this exercise is to give you a planning guide and a "to do list" for completing the exercises that will make it easier for you to stay away from alcohol and other drugs during the early stages of recovery.[3] It is important to keep your recovery as Job #1. You can do this by planning your treatment and recovery activities each morning and reviewing your progress and problems each evening. Starting today, please complete the Morning Plan and Evening Review on the list below and review it regularly with your doctor or therapist.[4] Today is Day 1!

Day 1: Day of Week _____ **Date** _____

Morning Plan

1. _____   4. _____

2. _____   5. _____

3. _____   6. _____

Evening Review

1. Did I complete my recovery activities for today?   ☐ Yes   ☐ No
2. Did I get into any high-risk situations?   ☐ Yes   ☐ No   ☐ Unsure
3. Did I have cravings today?   ☐ Yes   ☐ No
4. Do I need to talk to someone about my day?   ☐ Yes   ☐ No   ☐ Unsure
5. Do I need help to stay sober tonight?   ☐ Yes   ☐ No   ☐ Unsure

Day 2: Day of Week _____ **Date** _____

Morning Plan

1. _____   4. _____

2. _____   5. _____

3. _____   6. _____

Evening Review

1. Did I complete my recovery activities for today?   ☐ Yes   ☐ No
2. Did I get into any high-risk situations?   ☐ Yes   ☐ No   ☐ Unsure
3. Did I have cravings today?   ☐ Yes   ☐ No
4. Do I need to talk to someone about my day?   ☐ Yes   ☐ No   ☐ Unsure
5. Do I need help to stay sober tonight?   ☐ Yes   ☐ No   ☐ Unsure

Day 3: Day of Week _____ **Date** _____

Morning Plan

1. _____   4. _____

2. _____   5. _____

3. _____   6. _____

Evening Review

1. Did I complete my recovery activities for today?   ☐ Yes   ☐ No
2. Did I get into any high-risk situations?   ☐ Yes   ☐ No   ☐ Unsure
3. Did I have cravings today?   ☐ Yes   ☐ No
4. Do I need to talk to someone about my day?   ☐ Yes   ☐ No   ☐ Unsure
5. Do I need help to stay sober tonight?   ☐ Yes   ☐ No   ☐ Unsure

Day 4: Day of Week _____ **Date** _____

Morning Plan

1. _____   4. _____

2. _____   5. _____

3. _____   6. _____

Evening Review

1. Did I complete my recovery activities for today?   ☐ Yes   ☐ No
2. Did I get into any high-risk situations?   ☐ Yes   ☐ No   ☐ Unsure
3. Did I have cravings today?   ☐ Yes   ☐ No
4. Do I need to talk to someone about my day?   ☐ Yes   ☐ No   ☐ Unsure
5. Do I need help to stay sober tonight?   ☐ Yes   ☐ No   ☐ Unsure

Day 5: Day of Week _____ **Date** _____

Morning Plan

1. _____   4. _____

2. _____   5. _____

3. _____   6. _____

Evening Review

1. Did I complete my recovery activities for today?   ☐ Yes   ☐ No
2. Did I get into any high-risk situations?   ☐ Yes   ☐ No   ☐ Unsure
3. Did I have cravings today?   ☐ Yes   ☐ No
4. Do I need to talk to someone about my day?   ☐ Yes   ☐ No   ☐ Unsure
5. Do I need help to stay sober tonight?   ☐ Yes   ☐ No   ☐ Unsure

Day 6: Day of Week _____ **Date** _____

Morning Plan

1. _____   4. _____

2. _____   5. _____

3. _____   6. _____

Evening Review

1. Did I complete my recovery activities for today?   ☐ Yes   ☐ No
2. Did I get into any high-risk situations?   ☐ Yes   ☐ No   ☐ Unsure
3. Did I have cravings today?   ☐ Yes   ☐ No
4. Do I need to talk to someone about my day?   ☐ Yes   ☐ No   ☐ Unsure
5. Do I need help to stay sober tonight?   ☐ Yes   ☐ No   ☐ Unsure

Day 7: Day of Week _____ **Date** _____

Morning Plan

1. _____   4. _____

2. _____   5. _____

3. _____   6. _____

Evening Review

1. Did I complete my recovery activities for today?   ☐ Yes   ☐ No
2. Did I get into any high-risk situations?   ☐ Yes   ☐ No   ☐ Unsure
3. Did I have cravings today?   ☐ Yes   ☐ No
4. Do I need to talk to someone about my day?   ☐ Yes   ☐ No   ☐ Unsure
5. Do I need help to stay sober tonight?   ☐ Yes   ☐ No   ☐ Unsure

Day 8: Day of Week _____ **Date** _____

Morning Plan

1. _____   4. _____

2. _____   5. _____

3. _____   6. _____

Evening Review

1. Did I complete my recovery activities for today?   ☐ Yes   ☐ No
2. Did I get into any high-risk situations?   ☐ Yes   ☐ No   ☐ Unsure
3. Did I have cravings today?   ☐ Yes   ☐ No

4. Do I need to talk to someone about my day? ☐ Yes ☐ No ☐ Unsure
5. Do I need help to stay sober tonight? ☐ Yes ☐ No ☐ Unsure

Day 9: Day of Week _____ Date _____

Morning Plan

1. _____ 4. _____
2. _____ 5. _____
3. _____ 6. _____

Evening Review

1. Did I complete my recovery activities for today? ☐ Yes ☐ No
2. Did I get into any high-risk situations? ☐ Yes ☐ No ☐ Unsure
3. Did I have cravings today? ☐ Yes ☐ No
4. Do I need to talk to someone about my day? ☐ Yes ☐ No ☐ Unsure
5. Do I need help to stay sober tonight? ☐ Yes ☐ No ☐ Unsure

Day 10: Day of Week _____ Date _____

Morning Plan

1. _____ 4. _____
2. _____ 5. _____
3. _____ 6. _____

Evening Review

1. Did I complete my recovery activities for today? ☐ Yes ☐ No
2. Did I get into any high-risk situations? ☐ Yes ☐ No ☐ Unsure
3. Did I have cravings today? ☐ Yes ☐ No
4. Do I need to talk to someone about my day? ☐ Yes ☐ No ☐ Unsure
5. Do I need help to stay sober tonight? ☐ Yes ☐ No ☐ Unsure

Day 11: Day of Week _____ Date _____

Morning Plan

1. _____ 4. _____
2. _____ 5. _____
3. _____ 6. _____

Evening Review

1. Did I complete my recovery activities for today? ☐ Yes ☐ No

2. Did I get into any high-risk situations? ☐ Yes ☐ No ☐ Unsure
3. Did I have cravings today? ☐ Yes ☐ No
4. Do I need to talk to someone about my day? ☐ Yes ☐ No ☐ Unsure
5. Do I need help to stay sober tonight? ☐ Yes ☐ No ☐ Unsure

Day 12: Day of Week _____ Date _____

Morning Plan

1. _____ 4. _____

2. _____ 5. _____

3. _____ 6. _____

Evening Review

1. Did I complete my recovery activities for today? ☐ Yes ☐ No
2. Did I get into any high-risk situations? ☐ Yes ☐ No ☐ Unsure
3. Did I have cravings today? ☐ Yes ☐ No
4. Do I need to talk to someone about my day? ☐ Yes ☐ No ☐ Unsure
5. Do I need help to stay sober tonight? ☐ Yes ☐ No ☐ Unsure

Day 13: Day of Week _____ Date _____

Morning Plan

1. _____ 4. _____

2. _____ 5. _____

3. _____ 6. _____

Evening Review

1. Did I complete my recovery activities for today? ☐ Yes ☐ No
2. Did I get into any high-risk situations? ☐ Yes ☐ No ☐ Unsure
3. Did I have cravings today? ☐ Yes ☐ No
4. Do I need to talk to someone about my day? ☐ Yes ☐ No ☐ Unsure
5. Do I need help to stay sober tonight? ☐ Yes ☐ No ☐ Unsure

Day 14: Day of Week _____ Date _____

Morning Plan

1. _____ 4. _____

2. _____ 5. _____

3. _____ 6. _____

Evening Review

1. Did I complete my recovery activities for today?   ☐ Yes   ☐ No
2. Did I get into any high-risk situations?   ☐ Yes   ☐ No   ☐ Unsure
3. Did I have cravings today?   ☐ Yes   ☐ No
4. Do I need to talk to someone about my day?   ☐ Yes   ☐ No   ☐ Unsure
5. Do I need help to stay sober tonight?   ☐ Yes   ☐ No   ☐ Unsure

Exercise 2:
Understanding and Recognizing Addiction

Addiction is a brain disease that causes three abnormal brain chemistry reactions that make it easy for addicted people to keep using alcohol or other drugs while making it difficult for them to stop and stay stopped.

When addicted people use alcohol or other drugs they experience an **Addictive Brain Response**[5] that floods the brain with pleasure chemicals that make them feel good and deprive the brain of warning chemicals, which takes away feelings of stress, anxiety, and fear. When they stop using alcohol and other drugs, the brain does not just go back to normal. There is a rebound in brain chemistry that causes the levels of pleasure chemicals in the brain to go up and down in a chaotic and unpredictable way.

First, the brain stops producing the pleasure chemicals that are flooding the brain. This causes the level of pleasure chemicals to drop rapidly. They often drop so fast that they go below the normal level before the brain turns production back on. Then the brain turns the production of the warning chemicals back on. This causes the level of warning chemicals to increase rapidly. The warning chemicals often rise above normal levels before the brain slows down production. This creates a feeling of threat and anxiety. As a result, there is a period when the brain chemistry is unstable and fluctuating. The brain swings from not having enough pleasure chemicals to feel normal, to having a flood of pleasure chemicals that creates a feeling of euphoria. At the same time, the brain swings from having so many warning chemicals that we feel paranoid and hypervigilant; to having so few warning chemicals that we feel an unrealistic sense of courage and confidence.

This process keeps reversing itself. The pleasure chemicals spike back up creating a sudden sense of well-being and the warning chemicals drop back down taking away stress, anxiety, and fear. Levels of brain chemicals keep shifting back and forth from too high to too low until the brain eventually gets back to a normal balance. These fluctuations in brain chemistry make people feel agitated and depressed. They have problems thinking clearly and solving usually simple problems. Emotionally, people shift from being overreactive to feeling numb. This causes trouble in controlling behavior and may cause people to do things they normally would not do. People may experience memory problems and have trouble sleeping restfully. As addicted people use more alcohol and other drugs over a longer period, their symptoms keep getting worse and lasting longer.

The feeling of euphoria caused by alcohol or other drug use makes it hard for addicted people to believe that alcohol or other drugs are damaging the brain. The symptoms of *progressive brain dysfunction* become clear when addicted people try to stop using alcohol or other drugs. They experience craving, irritability, difficulty thinking clearly, difficulty sleeping, and agitated depression when they stop using.

There is often a progression from use, to abuse, to addiction.[6] Here is how it works:

- **Non-problem Use:** Addicted people often start using alcohol or other drugs in a casual and infrequent way that does not cause problems.

- **Frequent and Heavy Use:** The euphoric response feels so good that people at risk of getting addicted start using more often. They start to need to use more alcohol or other drugs to get the euphoric feeling they want. This is called *tolerance*. They use alcohol and other drugs for the euphoric effect and stop paying attention to how much they are using.
- **Abuse (Use that Causes Problems):** As the quantity and frequency of alcohol and drug use increases, people slowly start to have problems. They gradually move into a pattern of abuse. Remember, abuse is using alcohol and other drugs in a way that causes problems. Typically, these problems begin to affect family members, friends, and work.
- **Addiction:** They continue to use frequently and heavily until the alcohol or other drugs cause permanent changes in brain chemistry. Once the addiction is activated, there is no turning back. The addiction takes on a life of its own and will continue to progress through three predictable stages: early, middle, and late (chronic), as long as the person keeps using alcohol and other drugs.

The *early stage of addiction* is marked by a *growing dependency* on alcohol and other drugs. Early stage addicts are still able to feel good and function well. There are no serious problems so they see no need to cut back or stop. Their growing tolerance is forcing them to use more to get the same effect. Their high tolerance lets them use more without becoming intoxicated or having other noticeable problems. People in the early stage of addiction are often viewed by others as *heavy social drinkers* or *recreational drug users* who can handle alcohol and other drugs better than most people.

The *middle stages of addiction* are marked by a *progressive loss of control*. Sometimes when people start using, everything goes well. At other times, they use more than they intended to use to get the euphoric effect they want. Sometimes they use in moderation without getting into trouble or doing anything they are ashamed or embarrassed about later. At other times, however, they lose control, use more than they intended to use, and keep using for longer periods than they planned. Sometimes they miss important events because they lose track of time. Their judgment is impaired so they do things while drinking and drugging that they never intended to do. As a result, they start having problems and feel guilty and ashamed. This starts to happen more often, but there are still times when they can use without losing control and getting into trouble.

As the alcohol and drug-related problems become more severe, addicted people start to get scared, but are still having some good times. They become conflicted. A part of them thinks they might have a problem and should cut back or stop. Another part of them remembers how good it feels to use and how many times they have used in the past without getting into trouble.

They start having difficulty thinking clearly and avoid talking about their alcohol and other drug use or related problems whenever possible. If someone asks them about it or points out the problems they are having they get uncomfortable, change the subject, or tell outright lies. This is the beginning of serious problems with denial. *deep*

At this stage, addicted people begin avoiding sober and responsible people who tell them the truth. They start surrounding themselves with people who use alcohol and other drugs frequently and heavily. When they do have problems they deny them or rationalize them away. They start making solemn promises to themselves and others to stop, cut back, and to clean up their act. "I'll never get that drunk or stoned again," they promise themselves. They never define exactly how much is "that much." Therefore, when it happens again, they can rationalize the problem away. Then they forget about it, and forget they forgot. This creates the illusion that the problem never happened. In reality, however, the problems are happening and they are getting worse.

Finally, addiction moves into the *late* (*chronic*) *stages* that are marked by *progressive physical, psychological, and social deterioration*. Late stage addicts start having serious alcohol- and other drug-related health problems that keep getting worse. Psychologically, they are constantly feeling cravings, drug-induced euphoria, intoxication, anger, fear, guilt, shame, and pain. They do not want to think or talk about their addiction so they push other people away and start isolating themselves. If their friends or families get concerned, they brush them off, tell them some convenient lies, and give them the clear message to mind their own business.

They try to stop but cannot stay stopped. This destroys their self-confidence and self-worth. They start feeling ashamed of themselves and go underground. They try to hide what is happening, but by this time they are having serious physical, psychological, and social problems that are starting to catch up with them. They are having serious problems on the job or at school. The cost of maintaining their addiction is causing serious financial problems. They may also be having legal problems such as being caught drinking or drugging on the job, getting arrested for driving under the influence, or possessing and using illegal drugs. Prescription drug addicts use more than prescribed and start using more than one doctor to get the same prescription or they order additional medication on the Internet.

The problems keep getting worse until one of four things happens: (1) they die as a result of alcohol- or other drug-related illness, violence, or accidents; (2) they commit suicide to end the pain; (3) they get put in jail or committed to a mental institution; or (4) they get into recovery from addiction.

Addiction Symptom Checklist[7]

Read each of the following statements carefully. Put a check mark in front of the statements that are true or cause a conflict inside you. It is important to discuss your response to each question with your doctor or therapist.

☐ 1. I feel really good when using "the right amount" of alcohol, prescription drugs, or nonprescription drugs.

☐ 2. I have far less anxiety and fear when using "the right amount" of alcohol or other drugs.

☐ 3. It seems like nothing can hurt me, scare me, or make me feel concerned when I am using "the right amount" of alcohol, prescription drugs, or nonprescription drugs.

☐ 4. My personality changes, often in positive ways, when I am using "the right amount" of alcohol or other drugs.

☐ 5. Over time I needed to use more and more alcohol or other drugs to get the positive effect I wanted.

☐ 6. Sometimes when I look back, I can see that I used poor judgment or made mistakes I normally would not have made when I was using "the right amount" of alcohol or other drugs.

☐ 7. When I stop using alcohol or other drugs I find that I begin to experience problems thinking clearly, managing my feelings (I shift from feeling nothing to overreacting to little things), remembering things, and sleeping restfully. The longer I am abstinent the worse these symptoms get.

☐ 8. Sometimes my problems with thinking, managing feelings, remembering things, and sleeping get so uncomfortable that I want to start using alcohol or other drugs even though I would not start if I felt better.

☐ 9. I sometimes have problems as a result of my use of alcohol or other drugs.

☐ 10. I have made previous commitments to stop using alcohol or other drugs and have been unable to keep those commitments.

What It Means: The more items you checked, the more likely it is that you are addicted to alcohol or other drugs. If you have checked any of the items 1–4, you are probably experiencing the early symptoms of addiction. If you checked items 5–10 you are probably addicted. If you checked more than two items above, I strongly recommend that you ask your doctor or therapist to complete a formal addiction assessment administered by a trained and certified addiction professional.

It is easy to see the progression of addiction in other people. It is very difficult to see it in ourselves. That is why it is so important to understand denial. If you felt uncomfortable or felt an inner conflict when reviewing the above symptom checklist it could mean that denial is clouding your judgment. To stay abstinent during the early stages of recovery, it is important to learn how to recognize and stop denial so you can stay in touch with the need for treatment and recovery.

Exercise 3:
Making the Recovery Decision

1. What was the most important problem that caused you to enter treatment?

   _____

   _____

   _____

   A. If you continue to use alcohol or other drugs, this problem will probably…

   ☐ Get Better   ☐ Get Worse   ☐ Stay the Same

   B. Do you believe you need to stop using alcohol or drugs to solve this problem?

   ☐ Yes   ☐ No   ☐ Unsure   ☐ I don't want to answer

2. What are the most important problems that caused you to enter treatment?

   _____

   _____

   _____

   A. If you continue to use alcohol or other drugs these problems will probably…

   ☐ Get Better   ☐ Get Worse   ☐ Stay the Same

   B. If you stop using alcohol or other drugs these problems will probably…

   ☐ Get Better   ☐ Get Worse   ☐ Stay the Same

3. Did you identify with the description of addiction or any of the addiction symptoms on the addiction symptoms checklist?

   ☐ Yes   ☐ No   ☐ Unsure   ☐ I don't want to answer

4. Do you believe that it is in your best interest to stop using alcohol or other drugs at this time?

   ☐ Yes   ☐ No   ☐ Unsure   ☐ I don't want to answer

5. Are you willing to make an honest commitment to stop using alcohol or other drugs for the period of initial abstinence recommended by your doctor or therapist?

   ☐ Yes   ☐ No   ☐ Unsure   ☐ I don't want to answer

6. What things in your life will make it hard to stop using alcohol or other drugs even though you have made the decision to do so?

_____

_____

_____

7. Do you believe you could benefit from treatment designed to help you overcome the obstacles to stopping and staying stopped? Are you willing to accept a referral to a program that can provide that treatment process?

☐ Yes   ☐ No   ☐ Unsure   ☐ I don't want to answer

Exercise 4:
Making a Commitment to Abstinence

To recover from addiction you will need to become abstinent (stop using alcohol and other drugs). Although your doctor may prescribe medication to make your withdrawal more manageable, the goal is total abstinence. It is important to understand that detoxification alone, unless accompanied by ongoing medical and addiction treatment, often results in high rates of unnecessary relapse.

Below is a checklist of the most common reasons people go back to using alcohol or other drugs during the early stages of recovery. Read each statement and put a check mark in front of any that apply to you.

☐ 1. My stress levels keep going up and I cannot find any way to relax. This is because I am in the habit of managing my stress by using alcohol or other drugs.

☐ 2. I start feeling empty or numb and get so uncomfortable that I want to use alcohol or other drugs to start having feelings again.

☐ 3. I tend to emotionally overreact, get irritable, and easily angered. I want to use alcohol or other drugs to make these feelings go away or become more manageable.

☐ 4. I feel deprived because I cannot use alcohol or other drugs to cope with my stress, pain, and problems or to have fun and make life more enjoyable.

☐ 5. I start doubting my need to stay totally abstinent. I start having an inner internal conflict. One part of me tells myself that I need to be abstinent to get my health and my life back. Another part of me believes that I could stop treatment and just cut back and control my use.

☐ 6. I start having cravings. Cravings are the strong irrational urges to use alcohol or other drugs despite my problems that resulted from using. I want to start using again because it is the only way I know to temporarily make the cravings go away.

☐ 7. The original problems that caused me to seek treatment seem less important as the immediate crisis and problems start getting better. I actually have trouble remembering how bad things really were.

☐ 8. I start remembering the "good times" associated with using alcohol or other drugs and imagine that the good times were better than they really were. This makes me want to start using to have those good times again.

☐ 9. I have trouble remembering the pain and problems caused by my alcohol and other drug use. This makes me wonder if I really need to be in treatment and abstain.

☐10. I lose the motivation to do what I need to do to stay abstinent and just feel like this is too hard.

☐ 11. I start to deny the seriousness of my addiction and minimize my past problems with alcohol or other drugs.

☐ 12. I develop a false sense of confidence in my ability to recover and succeed at life without further treatment. I feel this despite my past failures and having no concrete ideas about what I need to do to stay abstinent.

If you are experiencing any of the above problems tell your doctor or therapist immediately. If you do not catch these problems and mistaken ideas early, you can make the mistake of starting to use alcohol or other drugs again. This will be a major setback and force you to start the process of recovery all over again.

Making a Formal Commitment to Recovery

It is important for you to make a clear and honest commitment to become abstinent and protect that abstinence by talking to your doctor or therapist about the common problems that can lead you back to using alcohol or other drugs. Read each statement and check the box that matches your honest commitment to keep that agreement.

1. I agree to ABSTAIN from using alcohol or other drugs as long as I am receiving treatment.

   ☐ Strongly Agree   ☐ Agree   ☐ Disagree   ☐ Strongly Disagree

2. I agree to immediately tell my doctor or therapist about any problems or situations that may develop during my treatment that could cause me to start using alcohol or other drugs despite my commitment.

   ☐ Strongly Agree   ☐ Agree   ☐ Disagree   ☐ Strongly Disagree

3. I agree to immediately discuss with my doctor or therapist any cravings or urges to use alcohol or other drugs.

   ☐ Strongly Agree   ☐ Agree   ☐ Disagree   ☐ Strongly Disagree

4. I agree to immediately discuss with my doctor or therapist any thoughts or feelings I may have about wanting to stop coming to treatment sessions or stop participating in other recovery activities such as self-help groups.

   ☐ Strongly Agree   ☐ Agree   ☐ Disagree   ☐ Strongly Disagree

5. I agree that if I do start using alcohol or other drugs I will immediately report it to my doctor or therapist.

   ☐ Strongly Agree   ☐ Agree   ☐ Disagree   ☐ Strongly Disagree

6. I understand that if I am caught using alcohol or other drugs before I report it to my doctor or therapist, it will be viewed as a deliberate act of deception and I may be terminated from treatment.

   ☐ Strongly Agree   ☐ Agree   ☐ Disagree   ☐ Strongly Disagree

7. I agree to submit to alcohol and other drug testing on a random basis and at the discretion of my doctor or therapist and that refusing to do so will be interpreted as an admission that I have been using alcohol or other drugs but refuse to admit it.

   ☐ Strongly Agree   ☐ Agree   ☐ Disagree   ☐ Strongly Disagree

8. I will consult the doctor monitoring my addiction treatment regarding the use of any medications prescribed by another physician to assure the medication will not interfere with my addiction treatment.

   ☐ Strongly Agree   ☐ Agree   ☐ Disagree   ☐ Strongly Disagreee

Exercise 5:
Managing Stress

Stress management is a vital key to staying away from alcohol and other drugs[8,] [9]during the early stages of recovery.[10] It is important for people in recovery to learn how to recognize their stress levels and use immediate relaxation techniques to lower their stress.[11, 12]

Recovering people are especially vulnerable to stress.[13] There is a growing body of evidence that many addicted people have brain chemistry imbalances that make it difficult for them to manage stress in early recovery. The regular and heavy use of alcohol and other drugs can have a toxic effect on the brain, creating symptoms that cause additional stress and interfere with effective stress management.

Many people who are in recovery from addiction have serious problems with Post-Acute Withdrawal (PAW). PAW is a biopsychosocial syndrome that results from the combination of brain dysfunction caused by addictive alcohol or drug use and the stress of coping with life without drugs or alcohol. PAW is caused by brain chemistry imbalances related to addiction. PAW disrupts the ability to think clearly, manage feelings and emotions, manage stress, and self-regulate behavior.

PAW is stress-sensitive. Getting into recovery causes a great deal of stress. Many recovering people never learn to manage stress without using alcohol or other drugs. Stress makes the brain dysfunction in early recovery get worse. As the level of stress goes up, the severity of PAW symptoms increases. As PAW symptoms get worse, recovering people start losing their ability to effectively manage their stress. As a result, they are locked into constant states of high stress that cause them to go between emotional numbness and emotional overreaction. Since high stress is linked to getting relief by self-medicating stress with alcohol or other drugs, high stress gets linked with the craving for alcohol or other drugs. So, one of the first steps in managing craving is to learn how to relax and lower stress without using alcohol or other drugs.

The severity of PAW depends on two things: the severity of brain dysfunction caused by addiction and the amount of stress experienced in recovery. The early stages of recovery is the period of highest stress in recovery. This high stress occurs before you have a chance to learn how to manage it in a sober and responsible way. Since you cannot remove yourself from all stressful situations, you need to prepare yourself to handle them when they occur. It is not the situation that causes stress; it is your reaction to the situation.

According to the National Institute on Drug Abuse, exposure to stress is one of the most powerful triggers for relapse to substance abuse in addicted persons, even after long periods of abstinence. Stress can cause a problem drinker to drink more, a person using prescription medication to use more than prescribed, and an illicit drug user to get more deeply involved in the drug culture than they could ever imagine. The high stress of the early stages of recovery can activate powerful cravings that make people want to start self-medicating with alcohol or other drugs despite their commitment to stop and stay stopped.

There is a simple tool called the *Stress Thermometer* that can help you learn how to monitor your stress. There is also a simple immediate relaxation technique called *relaxed breathing* that can help you noticeably lower your stress in two to three minutes. First, let's talk about the Stress Thermometer.

The Stress Thermometer

The Stress Thermometer is a self-monitoring tool that teaches people to become aware of their current stress levels, notice increases and decreases in stress at different times, and encourages the use of immediate relaxation techniques to lower stress as soon as stress levels begin to rise. The Stress Thermometer makes it possible to manage stress before craving for alcohol or other drugs is activated. Lowering stress can also lower cravings. Lowering cravings can help people turn off denial and addictive thinking. (More about this later.)

The concept of using a Stress Thermometer came from thinking about how you use a temperature thermometer to measure your body temperature. When you take your body temperature you use a thermometer to tell you accurately and objectively what your body temperature is. When you use a Stress Thermometer, you use a system to self-monitor your stress levels to tell you accurately and objectively how high your stress levels are.

The Stress Thermometer is divided into four color-coded regions: blue—*relaxation,* green—*functional,* yellow—*acute stress reaction,* and red—*trauma reaction.*

What the Stress Levels Mean

Low Stress/Relaxation: Stress levels 1, 2, and 3. These stress levels are coded blue because they are cool and relaxing.

- **Stress Level 1—Deeply Relaxed/Nearly Asleep:** At stress level 1 you are in a state of deep relaxation and nearly asleep. Your mind is not focused on anything in particular and you feel like you are waking up in the morning to a day off and can just let your mind drift in the deeply relaxed state.

- **Stress Level 2—Very Relaxed/Not Aware and Not Focused:** As you come back from a state of deep relaxation you enter level 2, during which you stay very relaxed, but begin to notice where you are and what is going on around you. You can stay in that state and just be aware and deeply relaxed. Eventually you will either go back down to level 1 and then perhaps falls asleep or else you will move up to stress level 3.

- **Stress Level 3—Relaxed/Aware but Not Focused:** At stress level 3 you become aware and start to think about getting yourself back in gear and getting going. In other words, you are getting ready to "kick start your brain" so you can move into a functional stress level to begin getting things done.

By practicing the *relaxed breathing technique* (explained on page 29) most people can learn to put themselves in a relaxed state (stress level 1, 2, or 3), stay there for a few minutes, and then come back feeling refreshed and relaxed. It is important to remember that this will take time and practice. In our culture people are taught to work hard and burn themselves out. People do not get much training on how to relax. People who get a euphoric effect from using alcohol or other drugs do not need to relax. When they get the "right amount" in their system they shut down their stress chemistry, turn on the pleasure chemistry, and feel relaxed.

It is important to practice relaxation four times per day. I recommend linking it to meals:

Take five minutes to relax in the morning before breakfast, five minutes at lunch, five minutes at dinner, and five minutes before going to sleep. Taking stress breaks will make it easier for you to stay at a functional stress level and bounce back quickly from high-stress situations.

With that in mind, let's look at the *functional stress levels*.

Functional Stress: Stress levels 4, 5, and 6 designate the zone of functional stress. They are coded green because green is a color that represents "go." At stress levels 4, 5, and 6 we are experiencing stress levels that are high enough to give us the energy to get started, keep going, and get things done. The stress, however, is not so high that in interferes with what we are doing.

- **Stress Level 4—Focused and Active with Effort:** With effort we get focused and active.

- **Stress Level 5—Free Flow with No Effort:** We operate at high performance, a state of free flow with little or no effort.

- **Stress Level 6—Free Flow with Effort:** We can keep on going but it takes effort and we notice we are getting tired. It is called *free flow with effort*. This is a good time to take a short break if you can to get your stress level back down to a level 5.

Acute Stress Reaction: Stress levels 7, 8, and 9 are coded yellow. The color yellow represents caution. At stress levels 7, 8, and 9 you are experiencing an acute stress reaction. The word *acute* means immediate and severe. The good thing about acute stress is that if you notice it early and know how to relax, by taking a short break and using a relaxed breathing technique for example, you can lower your stress and get back to the functional zone. When you enter stress level 7 it means that your immediate levels of stress have gotten so high that you cannot consistently function normally. You are in danger.

- **Stress Level 7—Space Out:** At a stress level 7 you space out. Your mind goes somewhere else and you do not even know you are gone until your mind comes back on task.

- **Stress Level 8—Driven and Defensive:** At stress level 8 you are driven and defensive. Your stress chemical has been activated and you are running on an adrenaline rush that is keeping you compulsively on task. The problem is that if someone or something interrupts you, you become defensive and can easily move into stress level 9.

- **Stress Level 9—Overreaction/Survival Behavior:** At stress level 9 our automatic survival behavior starts to take over. The three basic survival behaviors that everyone has are: **fight** (irritated, angry, agitated); **flight** (anxious, fearful, panicked); and **freeze** (you feel an agitated sense of depression and indecision. You freeze up and cannot make a decision or move.) On top of these three core survival behaviors you learn more sophisticated survival behaviors from your family of origin, life experiences, education or special training in stress management, emergency management, martial arts, or combat. For that training to automatically come into play, you must have practiced it repeatedly until it became habitual. In sports, emergency services, police work, and military operations these are called trained responses. When your stress hits level 10 your brain won't allow you to rise to the situation. The emergency brain response will always lower you to the level of your training. In an emergency, all you can rely on are the automatic responses you learned to perform on cue without having to think about them.

Traumatic Stress Reaction: Stress levels 10, 15, and 20 are coded red. Red is for "stop." At this point your stress levels are so high that your brain and mind are at risk of shutting down. There are three levels of stress that can occur in the red zone of traumatic stress.

- **Stress Level 10—Loss of Control:** You automatically start using your survival behavior and cannot control it. You are on automatic pilot and will go through your learned survival responses one-by-one. It is important to remember that all people with serious alcohol and drug problems have conditioned themselves with a survival behavior called "seek and use drugs to handle this." So it is not unusual for a person at a stress level 10 to get into drug-seeking behavior and start using alcohol or other drugs.

- **Stress Level 15—Traumatic Stress:** At stress level 15 your stress is so high you cannot stay consciously connected with it so your mind plays tricks on you. You are acting on automatic pilot and often feel like you are watching yourself doing it. You may feel like you are floating out of your body and may begin perceiving things around you as bigger or smaller than they really are, or closer or farther away than they really are.

- **Stress Level 20—Dissociation/Unconsciousness:** When your stress level hits a level 20 your brain just can't take the high level of stress and fatigue. You either collapse into an exhausted state of stupor or restless sleep, move into a vivid fantasy world or a world of memories or dreams, or become unconscious.

Any time people experience a "level 10 plus" state of stress; it will take a while after the stress stops for the brain to start functioning normally. When this is a short-term period of adjustment it is called an acute trauma reaction. When it is a longer-term reaction it is called *post-traumatic stress disorder.*

If you have ever experienced a "level 10 plus" stress experience which can happen when you are the victim of crime or assault, in an accident, caught in a burning house, participating in combat, or confronted with a life-threatening event. it is important to discuss the experience with your doctor or therapist. This is especially important if the high stress experience you had causes problems you did not have before it occurred.

Measuring Levels of Stress

Notice that you are measuring your personal perception of stress, which is a combination of three things: (1) the intensity of the stressor (the situation activating stress); (2) your ability to cope with or handle the stressor; and (3) your level of awareness while you are experiencing the stress.

It is possible for you to score yourself very low on the stress thermometer even when your stress is very high. This can happen because: (1) you are distracted and involved in something else (like managing the crisis causing your stress); (2) your stress is so high that you are emotionally numb and do not know what you are feeling; (3) you have lived with such high stress for such a long time that you consider it normal; and (4) you have trained yourself to ignore your stress.

The first step in learning how to manage your stress is to learn how to recognize and evaluate your level of stress and by learning how to get back quickly to a low stress level by using a relaxed breathing technique. Let's start by looking at how you can improve your stress awareness.

Improving Stress Awareness

The best way to learn to be aware of your stress level is to get in the habit of consciously monitoring your stress level. You can do this by using a mental tool called the Stress Thermometer, (page 28). The first step is to imagine that you have an internal Stress Thermometer that starts in the pit of your stomach and ends in your throat. The lowest reading on the Stress Thermometer is one and represents a deep sense of relaxation that is so complete you want to fall asleep. At a stress level 7 or 8, your stress becomes so intense that you start shutting down, getting defensive, or avoiding the issue that is causing the stress. If you cannot manage or get away from the stressful situation, at a level 10 you lose control and start believing that you cannot handle the situation and that you or someone you love may be hurt or killed. These extreme feelings of stress are called *trauma*.

When most people hit stress level 7 or higher, they are not able to respond to constructive criticism or make sense out of their emotional experiences. At stress levels between seven and nine most people start acting compulsively, overreact to things going on around them, and start using automatic habitual survival behaviors that may or may not solve the problem and lower stress.

This is why it is so important for you to learn to recognize your stress levels when they start hitting level 7 and learn how to lower them quickly. You can do this by using an immediate relaxation response technique called *relaxed breathing* any time you notice your stress hitting a level 7 or above. Therefore, you have four goals in this exercise:

1. To learn how to get in the habit of noticing when your stress is approaching level 7 or 8;

2. To learn how to quickly lower your stress by using the relaxed breathing technique;

3. To figure out what is happening and how you are thinking and feeling about what is happening that is causing your stress to go up; and

4. To manage the stressful situation by responsibly getting out of the situation or learning how to manage your thoughts, feelings, and behaviors to allow you to stay cool and relaxed even though you are in a tough situation.

The Stress Thermometer

Developed By Terence T. Gorski (© Terence T. Gorski, 2011)

www.cenaps.com • www.relapse.org • www.facebook.com/GorskiRecovery

Level 20	**Dissociation/Unconsciousness:** I get dissociated and feel like I am floating out of my body. Things seem unreal, and I eventually pass out.
Level 15	**Traumatic Stress:** Stress overloads the brain and I go into a state of daze or shock and can only use automatic overtrained behaviors.
Level 10	**Lose Control:** Fight = Anger-based; Flee = Fear-based; Freeze = Depression-based.
	The Brain Shifts Gears
Level 9	**Overreact:** Anger, fear, or compulsion gets out of control and starts running my intellect.
Level 8	**Get Defensive:** I use automatic defenses; I start acting out compulsively. The ability to think becomes a servant to hidden fear, anger, and depression. Strong craving and urges are to fight, run, hide, find a rescuer, blame others, or lose motivation and hope.
Level 7	**Space Out:** My brain cannot handle the stress, turns off for a second, and I go blank and do not even realize it until my brain turns back on a few seconds later.
	The Brain Shifts Gears
Level 6	**Free Flow Activity with Effort:** I am getting tired and have to push myself to keep going.
Level 5	**Free Flow Activity with No Effort:** I am totally into what I am doing and get lost in the process. I am on automatic pilot.
Level 4	**Focused and Active with Effort:** I make a decision to dig in and get to work. It takes effort to get started.
	The Brain Shifts Gears
Level 3	**Relaxed—Aware But Not Focused:** I am relaxed and aware of what is going on around me. I am beginning to realize that I need to get going.
Level 2	**Very Relaxed—Not Aware and Not Focused:** I am so relaxed that I am not aware of what is going on around me. I am disconnected and do not want to notice anything.
Level 1	**Deeply Relaxed—Nearly Asleep:** I am so deeply relaxed that I am drifting in and out of a dreamy type of sleep state filled with active fantasy or daydreaming.

**The Most Important Stress Management Tool Is
the Conscious Awareness of the Rise and Fall of Your Stress Levels.
This is achieved through self-monitoring.**

Monitoring Your Stress—Body Awareness

Body awareness is a technique that allows you to recognize how your body physically reacts to stress. It can be a powerful skill to use in stress management because as you notice stress in different parts of your body, you will start to relax the part of the body you are noticing. With enough practice, your body will automatically start to identify and release stress before you become consciously aware of it. Muscle tension is the primary way your body lets you know you are experiencing stress. Consciously using a systematic body awareness technique whenever you think about it and at least four times per day will start you on the road to teaching your body to automatically recognize and release stress. Here is how the technique works:

Begin by closing your eyes. You will concentrate on one muscle group at a time, tensing and releasing and being aware of how tight the muscle is as you focus on it. If the muscle feels tight as you begin, this may indicate you store stress in this muscle. Begin with focusing on your toes and slowly move up your body. Tighten your toes and release, flex your calves and release, tighten your thighs and release, tighten your stomach muscles and release, fist your hands and release, tense your shoulders and release, clench your jaw and release, squint your eyes and scrunch your face and release. Any time you encounter tension in a muscle, record that muscle tension and be aware that you are holding stress there. This will help you develop a personal stress reduction plan and use exercises and techniques to release pent-up tension.

Reducing Your Stress—Relaxed Breathing

There are a number of relaxation methods. For the purpose of this workbook, I am going to teach the easiest and most effective. It is called *relaxed breathing.* It is so effective that military, police officers, and firefighters are taught to use it to lower their stress when responding to emergencies. Here is how it works:

Relaxed breathing, often called *combat breathing* in the military or *tactical breathing* by police and emergency responders, is designed to calm you down and help you relax both before and during stressful times. In terms of the Stress Thermometer, use relaxed breathing before a stressful situation to calm you down and get you ready to be at your best. Use relaxed breathing during a stressful situation to keep your stress from going above that critical level 7, where your brain turns off and automatic defensive behavior and cravings kick in.

Early in recovery, some of your highest stress will be caused by thinking about and talking about your use of alcohol or other drugs. The catch-22 is this—if you don't talk about it, the thoughts will keep coming back like ghosts in the night that haunt moments that should be quiet and restful. Each time you expel the ghosts by refusing to think and talk about the "real problems" the ghosts go away for a little while and come back stronger. Your denial and resistance are strengthened, the intensity of your craving goes up, and your ability to think rationally about what you need to do goes down. As a result, the voice of this "stress ghost" grows into a full-blown "stress monster" that can literally take your brain hostage and make you believe that self-medication with alcohol or other drugs is the best or only way to get back in control of yourself and your life.

Step 1: The first thing you need to do is convince yourself that you can manage and reduce stress without having to self-medicate. There is another way. That way involves learning how to control your breathing.

Step 2: Practice relaxed breathing in a safe environment when you are not stressed. Just go through the steps and get used to them.

Step 3: Get used to rating your stress level. Initially you may need to use the Stress Thermometer, but with a few practices (four times per day for three or more days) use of the scale will be an automatic tool you will use whenever you check your stress level.

Step 4: Take control of the process by stressing yourself out and then relaxing yourself using the relaxed breathing technique.

Sit in a quiet place where you will not be disturbed for 10 or 15 minutes. Take a deep breath and do a quick body check. Then on a sheet of paper write the word *START* and underneath or next to it rate your stress level.

For example, I would do a body check and write: **START = 6**. I am still relaxed and able to think and respond, but I am tired and on the edge of spacing out.

Step 5: Stress yourself out! You heard what I said. Think about the things you usually think about that raise your stress. Be sure to beat yourself up about your drinking and drugging, how stupid you were, the problems it has caused, and how you will never ever be able to repair the damage you have done to your life. Stop the process before your stress hits a level 9 or 10 and you go running out of the room. Then write the words *AFTER STRESS* and rate your stress level. Most people find it easy to raise their stress.

For example, after beating myself up for about 60 seconds I would write: **AFTER STRESS = 8**. I feel myself driving myself and notice the thoughts start to take on a life of their own. If someone interrupts me at this moment, I could easily overreact.

Step 6: Relax yourself! You heard me. Do what you need to do to relax. This is the problem for many people, especially people who use alcohol, prescribed medication, or other drugs regularly and heavily. They can stress themselves out easily enough, but other than self-medication, they have no way to calm themselves down. So try this:

Take a deep breath and hold it for a moment until your lungs feel just a little uncomfortable, hold your breath for a moment, and then exhale all the way out. Hold your breath for a moment with your lungs empty and then slowly inhale again. Start to breathe a slow rhythmic count of four: "**INHALE**, two, three, four; **HOLD**, two, three, four; **EXHALE**, two, three, four; **HOLD**, two, three, four." Then start the cycle over by inhaling to the count of four. Repeat the cycle five times. Imagine the stress gathering in your lungs as you inhale and hold. Imagine the stress releasing from your mouth as you exhale and hold. That's it.

Now rate your stress again. Look at the Stress Thermometer and see what happened. Then write the word *AFTER* followed by your stress rating.

For example I would write: **AFTER RELAXING = 4** (remember I have been practicing a long time). So the record of my session looks like this: **START = 6**; **AFTER STRESS = 8**; **BREATHING REPS = 5**; **AFTER = 4**.

Do not force yourself to relax, just do the relaxed breathing, and focus on counting and visualizing the stress leaving your body every time you exhale.

Practice four times per day, at breakfast, lunch, dinner, and before bed. Keep track of your progress. Use relaxed breathing if you notice your stress going up during any of the following exercises.

Exercise 6:
Managing Denial

Denial is a normal and natural process used automatically and unconsciously by most people who develop serious problems with alcohol or other drugs. Just as the human body has an immune system to protect it from dangerous physical organisms, the human mind has a mental immune system to protect it from overwhelming pain and problems. That mental immune system is called a *psychological defense system*. The goal of the psychological defense system is to protect the integrity of one's mind and personality.

This exercise explains the basic information needed to understand and recognize denial so you can make a choice between continuing to lie to yourself or facing and dealing with the truth.

All people use denial from time-to-time to deal with problems that cause intense feelings of anger, fear, guilt, shame, and pain. This is because denial is a normal psychological defense that has both benefits and disadvantages. The major benefit of using denial is that it allows us to avoid feeling the pain caused by serious or overwhelming problems. The major disadvantage is that it prevents us from seeing what is really going on and effectively managing our problems. Fortunately, there are two antidotes for denial—accepting the truth about what is going wrong with our lives and developing effective problem-solving strategies to address our problems.

When you start thinking or talking about a problem you can do what is called a *denial check*. Let's do a denial check of your reactions to filling out the Addiction Symptom Checklist on page 17. Read each question again and after each question ask yourself five things:

1. Did my stress go up?
2. Did an inner conflict or argument start in my head?
3. Did I space out, get confused, or feel an urge to stop?
4. Did I start having intense feelings of anger, fear, guilt, shame, or pain?
5. Did strong painful memories come to mind?

If you find yourself answering yes to two or more of the above symptoms when you are thinking about or talking about a problem, there is a good chance you are using denial to avoid, minimize, or distort the problem.

The first step in learning how to manage denial is to learn how to sit still and notice what is going on inside of us. We need to learn how to notice what we are thinking, especially our inner conflicts and conversations, our feelings, and our urges to do things. By noticing what is going on inside of us, we can make conscious decisions about what we want to do before we blindly act out. Remember our goal: *to think it through before we act it out.*

Denial can be managed when it is recognized. Using denial is a habit. We can learn how to stop denial, look honestly at the problem, and set up a problem-solving plan. The first step is to recognize the feelings that are driving denial.

Monitoring the Feelings that Drive Denial

Strong feelings often cause us to avoid or deny the problems we have as a result of using alcohol and other drugs. As a result, we can easily be dishonest with both ourselves and other people. Please look at the list of feelings below that most people with alcohol or other drug problems experience when they first decide to recover.

When you think or talk about the problems that caused you to enter treatment, do you ever feel…

1. **Anger:** Caused by thinking, "People have no right to ask me about my alcohol, drug use, and related problems. I shouldn't have to think or talk about these things!"

    ☐ Yes   ☐ No   ☐ Unsure
    How intense is the feeling? (0 = not intense; 10 = very intense) _____

2. **Fear:** Caused by thinking, "I am facing difficult and seemingly overwhelming problems that are destroying my life. I'm not sure what will happen to me, my family, my career (job), and my life if I think and talk about my use of alcohol or other drugs and the problems I have had as a result."

    ☐ Yes   ☐ No   ☐ Unsure
    How intense is the feeling? (0 = not intense; 10 = very intense) _____

3. **Guilt:** Caused by thinking, "I have done something wrong by drinking and using drugs in a way that caused these problems."

    ☐ Yes   ☐ No   ☐ Unsure
    How intense is the feeling? (0 = not intense; 10 = very intense) _____

4. **Shame:** Caused by thinking, "I am a horrible and terrible person for doing what I did when using alcohol and other drugs. I must be defective as a human being because I have these problems. If I tell anyone about it they will judge me as a bad person and might even punish me or put me in jail."

    ☐ Yes   ☐ No   ☐ Unsure
    How intense is the feeling? (0 = not intense; 10 = very intense) _____

5. **Pain:** Caused by thinking, "It hurts so bad for me to face consequences of my alcohol or other drug use that I can't stand the pain of doing it."

    ☐ Yes   ☐ No   ☐ Unsure
    How intense is the feeling? (0 = not intense; 10 = very intense) _____

6. **Grief and Loss:** Caused by thinking, "It seems like I have lost so much that I will never be able to get back on my feet again. There are so many things that are gone that I will never be able to get back again."

    ☐ Yes   ☐ No   ☐ Unsure
    How intense is the feeling? (0 = not intense; 10 = very intense) _____

People can temporarily turn off these feelings by using denial, but the feelings almost always come back later. When the feelings return, they use denial again to make the feelings go away for a little while. Later, when the feelings come back again they use denial again. They keep doing this repeatedly until using denial becomes an automatic and unconscious habit for handling painful feelings. Since thinking and talking about serious problems almost always causes painful feelings, they actually get in the habit of using denial to manage problems and never learn other ways to solve problems. They use denial when they don't know any other way to manage pain or solve their problems. Most of the time they are not even consciously aware that they are using denial.

Recognizing Your Denial Patterns

Denial of having problems with alcohol, prescription medications, or illicit drugs is common. It is also dangerous. Denial keeps addiction going until people develop serious life and health problems. Denial can also cause people to convince themselves that they can start using alcohol and other drugs after they have started a recovery process. Once you see what you are doing, you can make the decision to stop using denial, to see the truth about your drinking and drug use, and make a commitment to recovery.

Please put a check mark in the box before any of the denial patterns you tend to use to keep from dealing with your problem with alcohol or other drugs.

☐ 1. **Avoidance:** I say to myself, "I'll talk about anything but my real problems!" I avoid thinking and talking about the problem with alcohol or other drugs. This convinces me that everything is OK.

☐ 2. **Total Denial:** I say to myself, "No, not me! I don't have a problem!" When others ask me to talk about my use of alcohol or other drugs, I tell "the big lie" by saying I don't have a problem. "No! Not me! Absolutely not!" I am so good at convincing other people that there is nothing wrong that sometimes I start believing it myself.

☐ 3. **Minimizing:** I say to myself, "My problems aren't that bad!" I make the problems seem smaller than they really are. "Yes, I had a small problem with my drinking and drug use, but it's not as bad as everyone thinks. Besides, it will never happen again."

☐ 4. **Rationalizing:** I say to myself, "If I can find good enough reasons for my problems, they will go away." So I spend time trying to "explain away" my problems instead of trying to figure out what is really wrong and how to fix it. I pretend to know what's going wrong but I really don't.

☐ 5. **Blaming:** I say to myself, "My problems with alcohol and other drugs are not my fault!" Other people and situations are making me drink or use other drugs. My problems are caused by my partner (or my divorce), my family (or living alone), my job (or not having one), my health (or lack of it), and so on. When these problem people and situations change, I will be able to stop.

☐ 6. **Comparing Out:** I say to myself, "I can't be addicted because other people use more than I do! I'm not as bad as they are so I must be OK." Addicts are not like me! They use more alcohol and other drugs than I do, and they have more problems than I do.

☐ 7. **Manipulating:** I say to myself, "I'll only say what others want to hear. I'll trick people into trying to help me even though I don't want help." When I get backed into a corner, I start to manipulate by tricking and using the people who want to help me. I'll let them help me, but only if they do it for me. I try to get them to handle all of my problems and get angry when they can't or won't. If they can't fix me, I blame them for my failure and use them as an excuse to keep drinking and drugging. I won't let anyone make me do anything that I don't want to do. If they try, I'll get drunk, blame them, and make them feel guilty.

☐ 8. **Compliance:** I say to myself, "I'll pretend to do what you want, if you'll leave me alone!" I do what I am told, no more, and no less. I make promises to get people off my back, but find excuses for not following through. I say that I did the best I could, tell people how sorry I am, and blame them for not giving me enough help. I ask for another chance, the cycle starts all over again.

☐ 9. **Flight into Health:** I say to myself, "Feeling better means that I'm cured!" I manage to stay clean and sober for a while, and things start to get a little bit better. I convince myself that I'm getting better because I never was addicted in the first place. I'm cured and don't need a recovery program.

☐ 10. **Recovery by Fear:** I say to myself, "Being scared of my addiction will make me recover!" I know that my addiction can kill me. I convince myself that fear will keep me from using alcohol or other drugs again. As a result, I don't need a recovery program.

Stopping Your Denial

Please select the three denial patterns that are most likely to cause you to start using alcohol or other drugs despite your commitment not to.

Denial Pattern #1:_____

What is a more helpful way of thinking about this? _____

_____

_____

_____

Denial Pattern #2:_____

What is a more helpful way of thinking about this? _____

_____

_____

_____

Denial Pattern #3:_____

What is a more helpful way of thinking about this? _____

_____

_____

_____

Exercise 7:
Managing Craving

In the early stages of recovery, people can be overwhelmed by powerful urges to use alcohol or other drugs (craving).[14] Part of the craving is caused by brain chemistry impairments that occur as a result of addiction. You can ask your doctor about medications that may be helpful to you. There are also powerful psychological and social factors that can cause craving or make it worse than it needs to be. In the early stages of recovery it is important to learn how to manage these psychological and social factors related to craving. Here is a three-stage model that has helped many people understand and manage craving:

Stage 1: Setup Behaviors

Ways of thinking, managing feelings, and behaviors that increase the risk of having a relapse.

Stage 2: Trigger Events

Events that activate the physiological brain responses associated with craving.

Stage 3: The Craving Cycle

A series of self-reinforcing thoughts and behaviors that continue to activate and intensify the craving response.

Recovering people unconsciously set themselves up to experience cravings. The setup behaviors lower their resistance to craving. When their resistance is down, they are vulnerable to trigger events that cause the actual urge or feeling of craving to start. Once they feel the urge to use, they start using habitual behaviors that amplify or make the craving worse. This is the craving cycle. Let's look at each of these three phases in more detail.

Physical Setups for Craving: Please put a check mark in the box in front of any physical setups below that you might experience during the early stages of recovery.

☐ 1. **Brain Dysfunction from Addiction:** Addiction to alcohol or other drugs damages the brain and leaves recovering addicts physically set up to experience powerful cravings. The result of this physical predisposition to experience cravings requires recovering addicted people to do special things to avoid craving.

☐ 2. **Poor Diet:** Recovering addicted persons are often nutritional disaster areas because they live on junk food and don't know what a healthy meal is.

☐ 3. **Excessive Use of Caffeine and Nicotine:** Both caffeine and nicotine are low-grade stimulant drugs and increase the likelihood of having cravings.

☐ 4. **Lack of Exercise:** Aerobic exercise reduces the intensity of craving and as a result can be a protective factor against craving, especially during the first two weeks of recovery. Check with your doctor and ask for a referral for exercises supervised by a physical therapist.

☐ 5. **Poor Stress Management:** When recovering people do not manage stress appropriately in recovery, they increase their risk of having cravings. Regular stress management activities such as meditation, relaxation exercises, taking regular breaks, and rest periods can help you prevent or manage cravings.

Psychological Setups for Craving: Please put a check mark in the box in front of any of the psychological setups below that you might experience during the early stages of recovery.

☐ 1. **Euphoric Recall:** Euphoric recall is a way in which addicted persons "romance the high" by remembering and exaggerating the pleasurable experiences of past alcohol and other drug use, while blocking out painful and unpleasant aspects of the memory.

☐ 2. **Awfulizing Abstinence:** When addicts awfulize abstinence, they notice all of the negatives and exaggerate them while blocking out all of the positive aspects of recovery. This leads the recovering addicted person to feel deprived in recovery and to believe that being sober is not nearly as good as using alcohol or other drugs.

☐ 3. **Magical Thinking about Use:** Magical thinking about use is the belief that using alcohol or other drugs will solve all of ones' problems. This magical thinking is brought about by euphoric recall ("Remember how good it was!"), and the awfulizing of sobriety ("Look how awful it is that I can't use it.").

☐ 4. **Empowering the Craving:** They exaggerate the power of the craving by telling themselves that they can't stand not having the drug and telling themselves there is no way to resist the craving.

☐ 5. **Denial and Evasion:** Addiction is a disease of denial. This denial does not go away simply because recovering people decide to stop using the drug. Many addicts deny that they need a recovery program to reduce the likelihood of craving. They also deny they are setting themselves up to have cravings. Denial is an automatic and unconscious process that causes many recovering addicts to believe they are doing the best they can in recovery when, in fact, they are not.

Social Setups for Craving: Please put a check mark in the box in front of any social setups below that you might experience during the early stages of recovery.

☐ 1. **Lack of Communication:** Recovering addicts often stop talking about their experiences in recovery and, as a result, they get into trouble. They replace rigorous honesty with superficial communication. This isolates them and prevents them from getting honest feedback about how they are doing in recovery.

☐ 2. **Social Conflict:** Many recovering addicts have a tendency to get into arguments and disagreements with other people. This social conflict can cause recovering addicts to avoid sober social situations and isolate themselves from others, spending more time alone.

☐ 3. **Socializing with other Drug-using Friends:** Out of loneliness and a desire to be with people who understand them, many recovering addicts decide to associate with people who they used to drink and drug with. This puts them in the proximity of the drug and sets them up to have a craving.

A. What are your primary setups for craving?_____

B. What can you do to stop using these setups? _____

_____

Identifying and Managing Trigger Events for Craving

Please put a check mark in the box in front of any social setups below that you might experience during the early stages of recovery.

☐ 1. **Thought Triggers:** Thought triggers arise out of addictive thinking or an addictive mindset that creates thoughts about the role that alcohol or other drugs play in a person's life.

☐ 2. **Feeling Triggers:** Feeling triggers come from sensory cues—seeing, hearing, touching, tasting, or smelling something that reminds one of alcohol or other drugs. It also results from experiencing feelings or emotions that were normally medicated by alcohol or other drugs.

☐ 3. **Behavioral Triggers:** The behavioral triggers deal with drug-seeking behaviors and rituals that activate a craving.

☐ 4. **Situational Triggers:** Situational triggers include any stressful relationships or situations that used to be engaged in on a regular basis while using alcohol or other drugs.

A. What are the primary thoughts that make you want to start using alcohol or other drugs?

_____

B. What can you do to avoid your primary triggers for craving?

_____

C. If you cannot avoid any of the triggers, what can you do to recognize and manage the craving early if it gets started?

_____

Breaking the Craving Cycle

Please put a check mark in the box in front of any social setups below that you might experience in the next two weeks.

☐ 1. **Obsession:** When the obsession is activated, the person has out-of-control thinking about alcohol or other drug use. Intrusive thoughts invade one's mind and he or she cannot turn them off. The obsession quickly turns into a compulsion.

☐ 2. **Compulsion:** When compulsion is activated the person begins to experience an overwhelming urge to use the drug even though they consciously know that it is dangerous to do so.

☐ 3. **Craving:** The obsession and compulsion merge into full-blown physical craving. Physical craving is marked by a strong desire to use the drug—rapid heartbeat, shortness of breath, perspiration, and at times the actual sense of tasting, smelling, or feeling the alcohol or other drugs. Physical craving is extremely powerful.

☐ 4. **Drug-seeking Behavior:** In an effort to manage the obsession, compulsion, and physical craving, many addicted people activate drug-seeking, ritual behavior. They begin to cruise old neighborhoods, talk with old drug-using friends, and go to bars and other places where alcohol and other drugs are used. This exposes the person to more triggers, which intensifies the craving cycle. Eventually, the person becomes overwhelmed with a compulsion they cannot control and they return to alcohol or other drug use.

Preventing Craving

You can prevent many episodes of craving by following these simple guidelines. Please check the box in front of the guidelines you are going to follow during the early stages of recovery:

☐ 1. **Recovery Program:** Develop a structured recovery program that puts you in regular daily contact with a doctor or therapist and other recovering people.

☐ 2. **Know Your Triggers:** Identify the things that activate the craving and learn how to cope with those triggers.

☐ 3. **Know and Avoid Setup Behaviors:** Know your setup behaviors and learn how to avoid or cope with those setup behaviors. If you do not set yourself up for craving, when you do have a craving it will be less severe and last for a shorter length of time.

☐ 4. **Dismantle Euphoric Recall:** Carefully examine past pleasant memories about alcohol or other drug use and search for the hidden negatives in the experience. Most people find they had no purely positive experiences while using alcohol or other drugs. There were always hidden negatives.

☐ 5. **Stop Magical Thinking:** It is also important to stop magical thinking about future use and to stop awfulizing your current sobriety. This will allow you to deal with the physical setups and let you know what to do to stop a craving.

Stopping Craving Episodes[15]

Since craving is a normal and natural symptom of alcohol and drug addiction that follows the addict into recovery, it is important for addicted people to learn how to deal with craving *in recovery*. This is done by learning and practicing a number of steps. Please check the box in front of the guidelines you are going to follow during the early stages of recovery:

☐ 1. **Recognize Craving:** Addicts must learn how to recognize a craving while it is happening. Many addicts fail to identify mild cravings as problematic and wait until they are in a full-blown, severe craving before taking action.

☐ 2. **Accept Craving as Normal:** Many people experience a craving or panic, and believe there is something wrong with their recovery or that they are condemned to return to alcohol or other drug use. This is not true.

☐ 3. **Go Somewhere Else:** The craving was probably activated by an environmental trigger, so get out of the setting you are in and get into an environment that supports sobriety.

☐ 4. **Talk It Through:** If you talk it through, you do not have to act it out. Addicted people need to talk about their cravings as soon as they occur to discharge the urge to use.

☐ 5. **Aerobic Exercise:** Exercise will stimulate brain chemistry and both reduce and interrupt the physiology of craving.

☐ 6. **Eat Healthy Meals:** Healthy and nutritious food will nourish the brain. Consume lean fish or meat for protein and eat whole wheat bread, baked potatoes, or brown rice for complex carbohydrates. Also taking vitamins and amino acids to replace the deficiencies that drug use caused will help stabilize brain chemistry imbalances.

☐ 7. **Meditation and Relaxation:** Cravings are worse when a person is under high stress. The more a person can relax, the lower the intensity of the craving.

☐ 8. **Distraction:** Divert attention from the craving by engaging in other activities that productively distract you from the craving feelings.

☐ 9. **Remember Cravings Are Time-limited:** The ninth step is to remember that most craving is time-limited to two or three hours. If you can use the previous eight steps to get yourself fatigued enough to fall asleep, most people wake up and the craving is gone.

Exercise 8:
High-risk Situations that Cause Craving

Relapse to the use of alcohol or other drugs is common in early recovery.[16] Please review the following situations that are often associated with craving and relapse to the use of alcohol or other drugs.[17, 18]

1. **Intense Emotional States:** Experiencing intense emotions that I believe I should not feel, I do not know how to manage effectively, or I have mismanaged in the past.

   A. How likely are you to experience a situation like this in the next several weeks? (0 = Not likely; 10 = Very likely) _____

   B. How confident are you in your ability to manage a situation like this without using alcohol or other drugs? (0 = Not at all confident; 10 = Very confident) _____

2. **Personal Pain:** Experiencing a situation that caused or will cause extreme discomfort, personal pain, injury, or illness.

   A. How likely are you to experience a situation like this in the next several weeks? (0 = Not likely; 10 = Very likely) _____

   B. How confident are you in your ability to manage a situation like this without using alcohol or other drugs? (0 = Not at all confident; 10 = Very confident) _____

3. **Pain of Others:** Witnessing the pain, illness, or injury of someone you know or love. This could occur by visiting someone who has been injured or seriously ill or witnessing an incident causing injury to others.

   A. How likely are you to experience a situation like this in the next several weeks? (0 = Not likely; 10 = Very likely) _____

   B. How confident are you in your ability to manage a situation like this without using alcohol or other drugs? (0 = Not at all confident; 10 = Very confident) _____

4. **Pleasant Social Events:** Being in a relaxing or pleasant social event or getting together with others for the purpose of celebration (such as a party, birthday, graduation, anniversary, or wedding).

   A. How likely are you to experience a situation like this in the next several weeks? (0 = Not likely; 10 = Very likely) _____

   B. How confident are you in your ability to manage a situation like this without using alcohol or other drugs? (0 = Not at all confident; 10 = Very confident) _____

5. **Unpleasant Social Events:** Experiencing a significant social event that marks an unpleasant, sad, or painful occasion. Examples include: funerals; divorces; losing cus-

tody of children; anniversaries of losses; holidays of emotional significance (such as Thanksgiving, Christmas, Hanukkah, Memorial Day, and Veterans Day); visiting military monuments, like the Vietnam Veterans Memorial, that stir memories of lost friends or loved ones; signing divorce papers; court actions such as finalizing divorce, bankruptcy proceedings, and other actions.

    A. How likely are you to experience a situation like this in the next several weeks? (0 = Not likely; 10 = Very likely) _____

    B. How confident are you in your ability to manage a situation like this without using alcohol or other drugs? (0 = Not at all confident; 10 = Very confident) _____

6. **Conflict with Others:** Having an upsetting argument or disagreement with others.

    A. How likely are you to experience a situation like this in the next several weeks? (0 = Not likely; 10 = Very likely) _____

    B. How confident are you in your ability to manage a situation like this without using alcohol or other drugs? (0 = Not at all confident; 10 = Very confident) _____

7. **Anniversaries of Losses:** Experiencing the anniversary of an important loss, whether you are alone or with others, that causes intense memories or feelings. Examples include anniversaries of life-changing injuries, deaths (especially the loss of a loved one), termination from a job, loss of career, or other major loss.

    A. How likely are you to experience a situation like this in the next several weeks? (0 = Not likely; 10 = Very likely) _____

    B. How confident are you in your ability to manage a situation like this without using alcohol or other drugs? (0 = Not at all confident; 10 = Very confident) _____

8. **Being around Alcohol or Other Drugs:** Being in places where you are around alcohol or other drugs or people who are using alcohol or other drugs. This could include such things as being home or in someone else's home knowing there are narcotic pain medications in the medicine cabinet, knowing there is liquor that you could have at your request, or dining at a restaurant where alcohol is available and nothing is there to discourage you from using.

    A. How likely are you to experience a situation like this in the next several weeks? (0 = Not likely; 10 = Very likely) _____

    B. How confident are you in your ability to manage a situation like this without using alcohol or other drugs? (0 = Not at all confident; 10 = Very confident) _____

9. **Social Pressure to Use:** Being around people who actively encourage you to start using and may think less of you, make jokes about you, or humiliate you if you don't.

    A. How likely are you to experience a situation like this in the next several weeks? (0 = Not likely; 10 = Very likely) _____

    B. How confident are you in your ability to manage a situation like this without using alcohol or other drugs? (0 = Not at all confident; 10 = Very confident) _____

10. **Testing Personal Control:** Purposely putting yourself around people, places or things that have caused you to use alcohol or other drugs to see if you can get through the experience without using.

   A. How likely are you to experience a situation like this in the next several weeks? (0 = Not likely; 10 = Very likely) _____

   B. How confident are you in your ability to manage a situation like this without using alcohol or other drugs? (0 = Not at all confident; 10 = Very confident) _____

What are the three high-risk situations that are most likely to make you want to start using during the next several weeks despite your commitment not to?

Situation #1 _____

Situation #2 _____

Situation #3 _____

Exercise 9:
Managing Thoughts

To manage high-risk situations that can cause craving we must learn how to identify the thoughts, feelings, urges, and actions[19, 20] that can make us want to use alcohol or other drugs. Let's start with managing thoughts. Think of the high-risk situation that you want to learn how to manage without using alcohol or other drugs.

1. Think of a time when you thought you wanted to use alcohol or other drugs, but did not *really* want to.

2. Keeping that situation in mind, read each of the thoughts listed below. Ask yourself if you tend to think similar thoughts when you are in this high-risk situation. If you do, put a check in the box in front of the thought. Check as many boxes as you need to.

   ☐ 1. I don't have a serious alcohol or other drug problem, so there is no good reason for me not to use alcohol or other drugs to deal with this situation.

   ☐ 2. I have a right to use alcohol or other drugs in this situation and nobody has the right to tell me to stop.

   ☐ 3. If I use alcohol or other drugs to deal with this situation, nobody will know about it. So what difference will it make?

   ☐ 4. If I use alcohol or other drugs to deal with this situation, nothing bad will happen to me as a result.

   ☐ 5. If I don't use alcohol or other drugs, I won't be able to effectively manage this situation.

   ☐ 6. If I don't use alcohol or other drugs, I won't be able to handle the stress and pain this situation will cause.

   ☐ 7. Alcohol or other drugs can help me manage this situation more effectively.

   ☐ 8. I should not have to do anything special to manage this situation. If I just go with the flow, everything will be OK.

3. What are the three thoughts that can make you want to use alcohol and other drugs despite your commitment not to? (You can use the thoughts above as a starting point, but it is important for you to put these thoughts in your own words.)

   Thought #1 _____

   • What is another way of thinking that would stop you from using?

   _____

   _____

Thought #2 _____

- What is another way of thinking that would stop you from using?

_____

_____

Thought #3 _____

- What is another way of thinking that would stop you from using?

_____

_____

Exercise 10:
Managing Feelings

1. When you start to feel the urge to use (cravings) do you tend to feel...[21]

   A. ☐ *Strong?* or ☐ *Weak?* How intense is the feeling? (0–10) _____

   B. ☐ *Angry?* or ☐ *Caring?* How intense is the feeling? (0–10) _____

   C. ☐ *Happy?* or ☐ *Sad?* How intense is the feeling? (0–10) _____

   D. ☐ *Safe?* or ☐ *Threatened?* How intense is the feeling? (0–10) _____

   E. ☐ *Fulfilled?* or ☐ *Frustrated?* How intense is the feeling? (0–10) _____

   F. ☐ *Proud?* or ☐ *Ashamed?* How intense is the feeling? (0–10) _____

   G. ☐ *Lonely?* or ☐ *Connected?* How intense is the feeling? (0–10) _____

2. What are the three strongest feelings you tend to have in the kind of high-risk situation that makes you want to use alcohol or other drugs?

   #1 _____ #2 _____ #3 _____

3. Evaluate your feeling management skills by reading each statement below and rating how true it is on a scale of 0–10 (0 = *not at all true;* 10 = *totally true*).[22]

   ____ Skill #1: I can anticipate situations that provoke strong feelings and emotions.

   ____ Skill #2: I can recognize when I am starting to have a strong feeling or emotion.

   ____ Skill #3: I can stop myself from automatically reacting to the feeling without thinking it through.

   ____ Skill #4: I can call a time-out in emotionally charged situations before my feelings become unmanageable.

   ____ Skill #5: I can use an immediate relaxation technique to bring down the intensity of the feeling.

   ____ Skill #6: I can take a deep breath and notice what I am feeling.

   ____ Skill #7: I can find words that describe what I am feeling and use the feeling list when necessary.

   ____ Skill #8: I am able to rate the intensity of my feelings using a 10-point scale.

   ____ Skill #9: I can acknowledge the feeling and its intensity by saying to myself, "Right now I'm feeling _____ and it is okay to feel this way."

   ____ Skill #10: I can identify what I am thinking that is making me feel this way and ask myself, "How can I change my thinking in a way that will make me feel better?"

____ Skill #11: I can identify what I am doing that is making me feel this way and change what I am doing in a way that will make me feel better.

____ Skill #12: I can recognize and resist urges to create problems, hurt myself, or hurt other people in an attempt to make myself feel better.

____ Skill #13: I can recognize my resistance to doing things that would help me or my situation, and I force myself to do those things despite the resistance.

____ Skill #14: I am able to get outside of myself and recognize and respond to what other people are feeling.

4. What is the *most intense feeling* you have that makes you want to use alcohol or other drugs? _____

_____

A. What are you *thinking* that makes you feel this way?

_____

B. What is another way of *thinking* that could make you feel different?

_____

C. What are you *doing* that makes you feel this way?

_____

D. What is another way of *acting* (something you could do differently) that could make you feel different?_____

_____

5. What is the *second most intense feeling* you have that makes you want to use alcohol or other drugs?_____

_____

A. What are you *thinking* that makes you feel this way?

_____

B. What is another way of *thinking* that could make you feel different?

_____

C. What are you *doing* that makes you feel this way?

_____

D. What is another way of *acting* that could make you feel different?

_____

6. What is the *third most intense* feeling you have that makes you want to use alcohol or other drugs? _____

_____

_____

A. What are you *thinking* that makes you feel this way?

_____

B. What is another way of *thinking* that could make you feel different?

_____

C. What are you *doing* that makes you feel this way?

_____

D. What is another way of *acting* that could make you feel different?

_____

Exercise 11:
Managing Behavior

1. Keeping a specific high-risk situation in mind, read the following list of *self-defeating behaviors* that can be used to mismanage a high-risk situation. Check the behaviors you are most likely to use:

    □ 1. **Procrastinating:** I put off dealing with the high-risk situation by finding excuses or reasons for not doing it now.

    □ 2. **Distracting Myself:** I get too busy with other things to pay attention to managing the situation.

    □ 3. **Saying "It's Not That Important":** I convince myself that other things are more important than effectively managing this high-risk situation.

    □ 4. **Thinking I'm Cured:** I convince myself that because I am OK now and don't have an alcohol or other drug problem there is no need to learn how to manage this high-risk situation more effectively.

    □ 5. **Playing Dumb:** Even though a big part of me knows what I need to do to manage this situation more effectively, I let myself get confused and convince myself that I can't understand what I am supposed to do.

    □ 6. **Getting Overwhelmed:** I feel scared and start to panic. I use my fear as an excuse for not learning how to manage the high-risk situation more effectively.

    □ 7. **Playing Helpless:** I pretend to be too weak and helpless to manage the situation more effectively.

    □ 8. **Wanting the Quick Fix:** I want a guarantee that I can quickly and easily learn to manage the high-risk situation more effectively or I will not even try.

2. List your three most harmful self-defeating behaviors and what you can do to change each behavior and do something different if you find yourself using it?

    A. Self-defeating Behavior #1: _____

    What is another way of behaving that could stop you from using alcohol or other drugs in this situation?

    _____

    _____

    _____

    _____

    _____

B. Self-defeating Behavior #2: _____

What is another way of behaving that could stop you from using alcohol or other drugs in this situation?

_____

_____

_____

_____

_____

C. Self-defeating Behavior #3: _____

What is another way of behaving that could stop you from using alcohol or other drugs in this situation?

_____

_____

_____

_____

_____

Exercise 12:
Evaluating Your Progress

As the last exercise in this workbook, I want you to think about where you were before you began this process, where you are now, and where you need to go to continue to make progress in your recovery and avoid relapse. To do this, please answer the following questions and discuss them with your doctor or therapist:

1a. **Morning Plan:** I am able to develop a morning plan that includes both my recovery activities and other daily activities.

   ☐ Not very true   ☐ Somewhat true   ☐ True   ☐ Very true

1b. **Evening Review:** I am able to review my day and make a sound decision about my need to call and discuss my day with another person.

   ☐ Not very true   ☐ Somewhat true   ☐ True   ☐ Very true

2a. **Understanding Addiction:** I am able to understand and accurately explain addiction to my doctor or therapist.

   ☐ Not very true   ☐ Somewhat true   ☐ True   ☐ Very true

2b. **Recognizing that I'm Addicted:** I know that I am addicted and I can describe the symptoms and life experiences with alcohol or other drugs that show that I am.

   ☐ Not very true   ☐ Somewhat true   ☐ True   ☐ Very true

3. **My Recovery Decision:** I have made a strong decision to recover from my addiction by abstaining from alcohol and other drugs and following the recommendations of my doctor or therapist.

   ☐ Not very true   ☐ Somewhat true   ☐ True   ☐ Very true

4. **My Abstinence Decision:** I have made a strong decision to abstain from alcohol and other drugs unless prescribed or reviewed and approved by the doctor who is treating my addiction.

   ☐ Not very true   ☐ Somewhat true   ☐ True   ☐ Very true

5a. **Knowing My Stress Level:** I am able to know what my stress levels are by using the Stress Thermometer.

   ☐ Not very true   ☐ Somewhat true   ☐ True   ☐ Very true

5b. **Lowering My Stress Level:** I am able to lower my stress level using the relaxed breathing or other relaxation techniques when my stress gets to level 7 or higher.

   ☐ Not very true   ☐ Somewhat true   ☐ True   ☐ Very true

6. **Stopping My Denial:** I am able to recognize when I am starting to deny my addiction, stop my denial, and make a renewed commitment to abstinence and recovery.

☐ Not very true ☐ Somewhat true ☐ True ☐ Very true

7a. **Recognizing My Craving:** I am able to recognize that I am having a craving as soon as the urge starts.

☐ Not very true ☐ Somewhat true ☐ True ☐ Very true

7b. **Managing My Craving:** I know what to do to manage the craving without starting to use alcohol or other drugs.

☐ Not very true ☐ Somewhat true ☐ True ☐ Very true

7c. **Confidence in My Ability to Stay Abstinent:** I am confident that I will be able to do what I need to do to stay abstinent if I experience a strong craving.

☐ Not very true ☐ Somewhat true ☐ True ☐ Very true

8. **High-risk Situations:** I know how to recognize and manage the high-risk situations that could cause craving.

☐ Not very true ☐ Somewhat true ☐ True ☐ Very true

9. **Managing My Thoughts:** I am able to recognize and manage the addictive thinking that could make me want to start using alcohol or other drugs.

☐ Not very true ☐ Somewhat true ☐ True ☐ Very true

10. **Managing My Feelings:** I am able to recognize and manage the intense feelings that could make me want to use alcohol or other drugs.

☐ Not very true ☐ Somewhat true ☐ True ☐ Very true

11. **Managing My Behavior:** I am able to recognize and manage the self-defeating be-haviors that could make me want to start using alcohol or other drugs.

☐ Not very true ☐ Somewhat true ☐ True ☐ Very true

12a. **Progress:** As a result of this self-evaluation I can see the progress I have made thus far in recovery.

☐ Not very true ☐ Somewhat true ☐ True ☐ Very true

12b. **Areas that Need More Work:** As a result of this self-evaluation I can recognize areas that I need to do more work on to increase my ability to stay abstinent and make prog-ress in my ongoing recovery.

☐ Not very true ☐ Somewhat true ☐ True ☐ Very true

12c. **My Ongoing Recovery Plan:** In the lines below briefly describe what you are going to do on an ongoing basis to stay abstinent and progress in your recovery. Review your ideas with your doctor or therapist. Ask them for additional suggestions and recommendations.

_____

_____

_____

_____

_____

_____

_____

_____

_____

_____

_____

A Final Word

Congratulations! You have now completed your first few weeks of recovery. You are part of a growing group of recovering people who have invested the time and energy to learn how to develop recovery skills and avoid relapse during the most difficult period in recovery. The exercises you learned by completing this workbook can be used immediately to help you identify and manage the most common problems that cause relapse. I hope that you will have begun an internalized system of dealing with life in a sober and responsible way that can be applied to many problems you will experience in your recovery.

Many of you will fully recover using your self-help program, counseling, and the recovery and relapse prevention skills you learned in this workbook. For some, however, these skills will not be enough. For some of you, especially those of you who were raised in a dysfunctional family, you may need to go beyond the contents of this workbook and learn how to identify and change the core personality and lifestyle issues that cause relapse later in your recovery after you have stabilized your health and initial problems.

The challenge of recovery is never really over. It seems that once we start a recovery process we are either growing or we are dying. There is no standing still. Either we commit ourselves each day to improving and refining our recovery skills, or we become complacent and slowly move toward meaninglessness, misery, and relapse. We must make a conscious choice each day about which path we will follow.

As you move from completing the workbook to using your new skills in real life situations, remember that temporary setbacks may occur, but you can always choose to get back into recovery. *Recovery is possible.* By completing this workbook, you have already taken a big step toward improving your recovery and lowering your risk of relapse. Your next job is to take the skills you have learned and use them in your daily life.

Remember, if you get stuck anywhere in the process you can always contact your doctor or therapist.

Good luck on your personal journey! I'm pleased and proud to have walked with you for a little while along the way. Thank you for permitting me to do so.

—Terence T. Gorski

Notes

1. **Definitions:** All the definitions are written to be easily understood by recovering people.

   Terence T. Gorski, *Straight Talk about Addiction: A Biopsychosocial Model.* (Independence, Missouri: Herald Publishing House/Independence Press, 2011).

2. This model is described in Terence T. Gorski, *Passages through Recovery: An Action Plan for Preventing Relapse.* (Center City, Minnesota: Hazelden, 1989).

3. **Relapse Early Intervention:** Methods based on symptom self-monitoring and self-management, when combined with regular professional monitoring of recovery, relapse warning signs, and the use of alcohol or other drugs (recovery checkups) can lower the rates of relapse and stop relapse quickly should it occur. The purpose of the morning plan and evening review is to get newly sober people into the habit of doing two self-checks per day and having a document to show healthcare providers to provide evidence that can be inspected to show they have been doing it. It also becomes a quick way to check for consistency, insights related to addiction recovery, and early indicators of lack of motivation or cognitive impairment. This is done by a simple review of the content of each morning plan and evening review.

   C. K. Scott, M. L. Dennis, and M. A. Foss, Utilizing recovery management checkups to shorten the cycle of relapse, treatment reentry, and recovery. *Drug and Alcohol Dependence* 78(3):325–338, 2005.

4. **Stress Management Model:** The basis of the stress management method used in this manual is consistent with a modified temporal difference reinforcement learning (TDRL) model that teaches people how to recognize the cues related to stress, craving, and relapse, with self-monitoring methods that help people recognize these cues, and simple techniques for breaking the association between the cue and the learned craving and self-medication response.

   A. D: Redish, S. Jensen, A. Johnson, and Z. Kurth-Nelson, Department of Neuroscience, University of Minnesota, Minneapolis, MN 55455, USA. Reconciling reinforcement learning models with behavioral extinction and renewal: implications for addiction, relapse, and problem gambling. *Psychological Review* 114(3):784–805, 2007.

5. **Addictive Brain Response:** In people who are at a high risk for addiction, the brain responds to their drug of choice with an addictive brain response that floods the brain with pleasure chemicals and then deprives the brain of warning chemicals. The flood of pleasure chemicals makes people feel really good by creating an intense feeling of euphoria. This deprivation of warning chemicals minimizes or blocks out the feeling of danger or threat. These warning chemicals normally flood the brain whenever we are in danger, facing a stressful situation or serious threat, or when we have a survival need like hunger or thirst. The job of these warning chemicals is to make people feel so uncomfortable that they start looking around to see what is wrong. When the addictive brain response slows down or stops the production of these warning chemicals, nothing feels threatening. Nothing scares us or makes us feel concerned. It seems like nothing

can hurt us. As a result, good judgment goes out the window and we can start doing dangerous things without even realizing it. The brain does not just go back to normal. There is a *rebound in brain chemistry* that causes the levels of pleasure chemicals in the brain to go up and down in a chaotic and unpredictable way.

First, the brain stops producing the pleasure chemicals that are flooding the brain. This causes the level of pleasure chemicals to drop rapidly. They often drop so fast that they go below the normal level before the brain turns production back on.

Second, the brain turns the production of the *warning chemicals* back on. This causes the level of warning chemicals to increase rapidly. The warning chemicals often rise above normal levels before the brain slows down production. This creates a feeling of threat and anxiety. As a result, there is a period when the brain chemistry is unstable and fluctuating. The brain swings from not having enough pleasure chemicals to feel normal, to having a flood of pleasure chemicals that makes you euphoric. At the same time, the brain swings from having so many warning chemicals that you feel paranoid and hypervigilant, to having too few warning chemicals that makes you feel an unrealistic sense of courage and confidence.

Third, this process keeps reversing itself. The pleasure chemicals spike back up. The warning chemicals drop back down. The chemistry of the brain vibrates like a guitar string as the levels of brain chemicals shift back and forth from too high to too low until the brain eventually gets back to a normal balance. These fluctuations in brain chemistry make people feel agitated and depressed. It makes it hard to think clearly. You have trouble solving usually simple problems. You either emotionally overreact or become emotionally numb and cannot tell what you are feeling.

> Terence T. Gorski, *Straight Talk about Addiction: A Biopsychosocial Model.* (Independence, Missouri: Herald Publishing House/Independence Press, 2011), 73–75.

6. **Alcoholism Assessment:** The history of alcoholism assessment has been well-documented by the National Institute on Alcohol Abuse and Alcoholism (NIAAA).

> National Institute on Alcohol Abuse and Alcoholism, Diagnostic criteria for alcohol abuse and dependence. *Alcohol Alert*, No. 30, PH 359, October 1995.

> National Institute on Alcohol Abuse and Alcoholism. Screening for alcohol problems—an update. *Alcohol Alert*, No. 56, April 2002.

7. **Addiction Symptom Self-Evaluation:** This diagnostic self-report tool is consistent with the criteria for substance dependence in DSM-IV-TR. It is a self-report tool and a validated diagnostic instrument.

> American Psychiatric Association, *Diagnostic and Statistical Manual of Mental Disorders DSM-IV-TR* (Text Revision), 4th ed. (Washington, D. C.: American Psychiatric Association, July 2000).

8. **Stress and increased Relapse Risk:** "Stress is an important factor known to increase alcohol and drug relapse risk. This paper examines the stress-related processes that influence addiction relapse. First, individual patient vignettes of stress- and cue-related

situations that increase drug-seeking and relapse susceptibility are presented. Next, empirical findings from human laboratory and brain-imaging studies that are consistent with clinical observations and support the specific role of stress processes in the drug-craving state are reviewed. Recent findings on differences in stress responsivity in addicted versus matched community social drinkers are reviewed to demonstrate alterations in stress pathways that could explain the significant contribution of stress-related mechanisms on craving and relapse susceptibility. Finally, significant implications of these findings for clinical practice are discussed, with a specific focus on the development of novel interventions that target stress processes and drug craving to improve addiction relapse outcomes." (Abstract, PMID: 17915078)

R. Sinha, Department of Psychiatry, Yale University School of Medicine, New Haven, CT 06515, USA. The role of stress in addiction relapse. *Current Psychiatry Reports* 9(5):388–395, 2007.

9. **Stress Identification and Management:** Relapse risk as verified by clinical observations, patient self-reports, and "subjective and behavioral measures such as depressive symptoms, stress, and drug craving" during withdrawal. All of these factors predict future relapse risk. "Among neural measures, brain atrophy in the medial frontal regions and hyperreactivity of the anterior cingulate during withdrawal were identified as important in drug withdrawal and relapse risk." This study suggests that stress management would be helpful in preventing relapse especially during the period of withdrawal. (Abstract, PMID 21792580)

R. Sinha, Department of Psychiatry, Yale University School of Medicine, New Haven, CT 06515, USA. New findings on biological factors predicting addiction relapse vulnerability. *Current Psychiatry Reports* 13(5):398–405, 2011. (*reference.medscape.com/medline/abstract/21792580*)

10. **The Role of Stress in Addiction:** Both animal and human studies demonstrate that stress plays a major role in the process of alcohol and drug addiction and that a variety of stressors can increase both self-reported stress and measures of biological stress. Among neural measures, brain atrophy in the medial frontal regions and hyperreactivity of the anterior cingulate during withdrawal were identified as important in drug withdrawal and relapse risk. This study suggests that stress management would be helpful in preventing relapse especially during the period of withdrawal.

New findings on biological factors predicting addiction relapse vulnerability. *Current Psychiatry Reports* 13(5):398–405, 2011. (*reference.medscape.com/medline/abstract/21792580*)

11. **Stress and Addiction:** Stress plays a major role in the process of drug addiction and various stressors are known to increase measures of craving in drug-dependent human laboratory subjects. Animal models of stress-induced reinstatement of drug-seeking have also been developed to determine the neuropharmacological and neurobiological features of stress-induced relapse.

R. E. See and R. P. Waters, Department of Neurosciences, Medical University of South Carolina, Charleston, SC 29425 USA. Pharmacologically-induced stress: a cross-species probe for translational research in drug addiction and relapse. *American Journal of Translational Research*, 3(1):81–9, 2010.

12. **Stress-induced Craving and Cognitive Behavioral Therapy:** The Division of Clinical Neurosciences, Medical University of South Carolina, Charleston, South Carolina 29425, USA (*backs@musc.edu*) has found that "stress-induced craving and stress reactivity may influence risk for substance use or relapse to use. Interventions designed to manage stress-induced craving and stress reactivity may serve as excellent adjuncts to more comprehensive treatment programs. The purpose of this study was to (1) tailor an existing, manualized, cognitive-behavioral stress management (CBSM) intervention for use in individuals with substance use disorders and (2) preliminarily evaluate the effects of the intervention using an experimental stress-induction paradigm. Twenty individuals were interviewed and then completed a psychological stress task, the Mental Arithmetic Task (MAT). After this, participants were assigned to either the CBSM intervention group or a non-treatment comparison group. Approximately three weeks later, participants completed a second MAT. In contrast to the comparison group, the CBSM group demonstrated significantly less stress-induced craving (p<.04) and stress (p<.02), and reported greater ability to resist urges to use (p<.02) after the second MAT. These findings are among the first to report on the use of an intervention to attenuate craving and stress reactivity among individuals with substance use disorders. Although preliminary, the findings suggest that systematic investigation of interventions specifically targeting stress management in individuals with substance use disorders should be undertaken." (Abstract, PMID 17700298)

S. E. Back, S. Gentilin, and K. T. Brady. Cognitive-behavioral stress management for individuals with substance use disorders: a pilot study. *Journal of Nervous and Mental Disease* 195(8):662–668, 2007.

13. **Research Society on Alcoholism:** "This report of the proceedings of a symposium presented at the 2004 Research Society on Alcoholism Meeting provides evidence linking stress during sobriety to craving that increases the risk for relapse. The initial presentation by Rajita Sinha summarized clinical evidence for the hypothesis that there is an increased sensitivity to stress-induced craving in alcoholics. During early abstinence, alcoholics who were confronted with stressful circumstances showed increased susceptibility for relapse. George Breese presented data demonstrating that stress could substitute for repeated withdrawals from chronic ethanol to induce anxiety-like behavior. This persistent adaptive change induced by multiple withdrawals allowed stress to induce an anxiety-like response that was absent in animals that were not previously exposed to chronic ethanol. Subsequently, Amanda Roberts reviewed evidence that increased drinking induced by stress was dependent on corticotrophin-releasing factor (CRF). In addition, rats that were stressed during protracted abstinence exhibited anxiety-like behavior that was also dependent on CRF. Christopher Dayas indicated that stress increases the reinstatement of an alcohol-related cue. Moreover, this effect was enhanced by previous alcohol dependence. These interactive effects between stress and alcohol-related environmental stimuli depended on concurrent activation of endogenous opioid and CRF systems. A. D. Lê covered information that indicated that stress facilitated reinstatement to alcohol responding and summarized the influence of

multiple deprivations on this interaction. David Overstreet provided evidence that restraint stress during repeated alcohol deprivations increases voluntary drinking in alcohol-preferring (P) rats that result in withdrawal-induced anxiety that is not observed in the absence of stress. Testing of drugs on the stress-induced voluntary drinking implicated serotonin and CRF involvement in the sensitized response. Collectively, the presentations provided convincing support for an involvement of stress in the cause of relapse and continuing alcohol abuse and suggested novel pharmacological approaches for treating relapse induced by stress." (Abstract, PMID 15714042)

George R. Breese, Kathleen Chu, Christopher V. Dayas, Douglas Funk, Darin J. Knapp, George F. Koob, Dzung Anh Lê, Laura E. O'Dell, David H. Overstreet, Amanda J. Roberts, Rajita Sinha, Glenn R. Valdez, and Friedbert Weiss. Stress enhancement of craving during sobriety: a risk for relapse, *Alcoholism: Clinical and Experimental Research*, February 2005; 29(2):185–195.

14. **NIDA Craving Management Strategies:** The basic science-based steps for managing craving are consistent with information presented in the NIDA Toolbox under Coping with Cravings. The key research-based recommendations are divided into three general strategies: Strategy 1: Recognize (Learn about and know what the triggers are and the early signs in thinking, feeling, and body sensations that tell you that you are starting to have a craving); Strategy 2: Avoid Triggers (Classify trigger events that cause craving under the general categories of people places and things. Evaluate what triggers for craving you can responsibly avoid.); Strategy 3: Cope with Craving (Learn and use relaxation methods and strategies for managing your thoughts, feelings, and actions related to a craving episode.). These three strategies are incorporated in the process of this workbook.

www.nidatoolbox.org

15. **Gorski Craving Management Model:** This model is summarized from Gorski's original pamphlet on cocaine craving and relapse. It has remained a good summary of the emerging science-based steps for managing craving since it was introduced over 20 years ago.

Terence T. Gorski, *Managing Cocaine Craving*. (Center City, Minnesota: Hazelden, 1990).

16. **Relapse Risk:** Individuals with substance use disorders are at high risk of relapse once they have stopped using alcohol and other drugs and started to recover. There is a strong need to train treatment facility administrators and clinicians how to properly implement Relapse Prevention (RP) methods within their treatment programs.

"Studies of lifelong patterns of recovery and relapse indicate that patients who relapse are not hopeless. (Valliant, 1983) Approximately one-third achieve permanent abstinence from their first serious attempt at recovery.

Another third have a series of brief relapse episodes that eventually result in long-term abstinence. An additional one-third have chronic relapses that result in eventual disability and death from chemical dependency." (5) "About one-half of all relapse prone persons eventually find permanent abstinence. Many others improve in spite of the periodic relapse episodes." (Vaillant, 1983; Marlatt, 1985; Pickens et al., 1985)

In 2002, there were more than 13,720 substance abuse treatment facilities within the United States providing treatment to approximately 1,136,287 patients. (SAMHSA 2003) All were treating relapse prone patients. In a typical publicly funded treatment facility, about 13 percent of the patients are chronic relapsers who have been admitted for substance abuse treatment five or more times, 58 percent are relapse prone patients who have been admitted for treatment between one and four times, and 29 percent are patients entering treatment for the first time. Of the patients entering treatment for the first time at least 60 percent are at high risk of becoming relapse prone. (SAMHSA 2002)

Treating relapse-prone patients imposes a significant cost on the health care system and other areas of society. The 1990 National Drug and Alcohol Treatment Utilization Study (NDATUS) estimated that the United States spent a total of $4.08 billion in treating people with substance use disorders. Since, at that time, about 40 percent of these patients were relapsers, the nations spent $1.63 billion treating relapsers in 1990. Unfortunately, most of this money was spent on recycling patients through treatment that had already failed. Little is spent systematically implementing proven relapse prevention technologies. (Terence T. Gorski. Relapse prevention: a treatment method comes of age, *Drink and Drugs News*, Sept. 11, 2006, *www.drinkanddrugsnews.com*)

After nearly 30 years of progressive development, RP has become a recognized and effective treatment method. A wide array of proven RP program models has been developed. (Daley and Marlatt, 1997)

What is needed is a systematic program to implement the current relapse prevention technology and encourage its use in existing treatment programs. Such implementation needs to be accompanied by appropriate measures of treatment outcomes to evaluate its effectiveness.

References for Relapse Prevention:

D. C. Daley and G. A. Marlatt, "Relapse Prevention," in *Lowinson and Ruiz's Substance Abuse: A Comprehensive Textbook*, 5th ed., Pedro Ruiz and Eric Strain, eds. (Philadelphia: Lippincott, Williams & Wilkins, 2011).

SAMHSA (Substance Abuse and Mental Health Services Administration), Office of Applied Studies. *National Survey of Substance Abuse Treatment Services (N-SSATS): 2002B. Data on Substance Abuse Treatment Facilities*, DASIS Series: S-19, DHHS Publication No. (SMA) 03-3777, Rockville, MD, 2003. (*wwwdasis.samhsa.gov/02nssats/nssats2002report.pdf*)

SAMHSA Advance Report Number 9: The National Drug and Alcoholism Treatment Unit Survey (NDATUS): 1992 and 1980–1992, Substance Abuse and Mental Health

Services Administration Office of Applied Studies, U.S. Department of Health and Human Services Public Health Service, January 1995. (*ncadi.samhsa.gov/govpubs/ar013/default.aspx*)

G. E. Vaillant, *The Natural History of Alcoholism: Causes, Patterns, and Paths to Recovery.* (Cambridge, Massachusetts: Harvard University Press, 1983).

17. **Relapse Warning Signs:** The idea that relapse is preceded by progressive relapse warning signs has been long-recognized by Gorski's model of relapse prevention. Although based on clinical observation and self-report questionnaires, this model has gained acceptance and continues to be used by treatment centers. The original publications containing Gorski's relapse warning signs are listed below:

Terence T. Gorski, *The Dynamics of Relapse in the Alcoholic Patient.* (Harvey, Illinois: Ingalls Memorial Hospital, 1(9):1–18, September 1976).

Terence T. Gorski and Merlene M. Miller, *Counseling for Relapse Prevention: The Workshop Manual.* (Hazel Crest, Illinois: Human Ecology Systems, Inc., 1979).

Terence T. Gorski, Dynamics of relapse. *EAP Digest*, November/December 1980; 16–21, 45–49.

Terence T. Gorski and Merlene Miller, *The Phases and Warning Signs of Relapse.* (Independence, Missouri: Herald Publishing House/Independence Press, 1999).

Terence T. Gorski and Merlene Miller, *Counseling for Relapse Prevention.* (Independence, Missouri: Herald Publishing House, 1982), 43–75.

18. **High-risk Situations:** The general categories of high-risk situations used in this workbook were first identified by G. A. Marlatt in 1985.

G. Alan Marlatt. "Relapse Prevention: Theoretical Rationale and Overview of the Model" in *Relapse Prevention—Maintenance Strategies in the Treatment of Addictive Behaviors*, G. Alan Marlatt and Judith R. Gordon, eds. (New York: The Guilford Press, 1985), 3–70.

19. **NIDA—Cognitive-Behavioral Approach:** A four-step standardized method that follows involves managing thoughts (T), feelings (F), urges (U), and actions (A). This model has become a standard part of advanced clinical skills training for doing cognitive restructuring with any problem. This is consistent with NIDA approaches: This approach is fully described in NIDA Therapy Manuals and the underlying treatment methodology are consistent with those presented in the manual listed below. Cognitive-behavioral therapy is the strongest science-based methodology for psychotherapy of alcohol- and drug-dependent clients.

National Institute for Drug Abuse: NIDA Therapy Manuals for Drug Abuse: Manual 2—Cognitive-Behavioral Approach: Treating Cocaine Addiction (*archives.drugabuse.gov/TXManuals/CBT/CBT8.html*)

20. **Cognitive Restructuring for Addiction:** Gorski introduced a standard and simplified a cognitive restructuring method that is the core underlying method in all of his clinical workbooks. This method was generalized and made explicit in 2004.

Terence T. Gorski, *Cognitive Restructuring for Addiction Workbook*. (Independence, Missouri: Herald Publishing House/Independence Press, 2004).

21. **Feeling Identification and Management:** This model for feeling identification and management has been used since this book was first published in 1998. Since 1998 this model has been consistent, with minor modifications, and was most recently published in Gorski's, *Relapse Prevention Therapy Workbook*.

Terence T. Gorski, *The Staying Sober Workbook—A Serious Solution for the Problem of Relapse, Rev. ed.* (Independence, Missouri: Herald Publishing House/Independence Press, 1992).

22. **Feeling Management Skills:** The feeling management skills described in this part of the exercise are supported by the accumulated research of Goleman.

Daniel Goleman, *Emotional Intelligence*, 10th ed., (New York: Bantam, 2006).

Additional Resources

Terence T. Gorski and The CENAPS Corporation have developed extensive resources for relapse prevention and recovery. Learn more about these resources at: *www.cenaps.com*, *www.relapse.org*, or *www.facebook.com/GorskiRecovery*.